Garfield
In Training

JIM DAVIS

RAVETTE PUBLISHING

© 1994 Paws, Incorporated
All rights reserved

First published by
Ravette Books Limited 1994
Reprinted by Ravette Publishing Limited 1995
Reprinted 1996

Printed and bound in Great Britain
for Ravette Publishing Limited,
Unit 3, Tristar Centre,
Star Road, Partridge Green,
West Sussex RH13 8RA
by Cox & Wyman Ltd, Reading, Berkshire

ISBN 1 85304 785 6

© 1992 United Feature Syndicate, Inc.

BONKA
BONKA
BONKA
BONKA
BONKA
BONKA
THUD!

© 1992 United Feature Syndicate, Inc.

© 1993 United Feature Syndicate, Inc.

© 1993 United Feature Syndicate, Inc.

JIM DAVIS 1-27

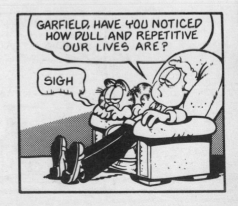

SHOW-OFF

JIM DAVIS 2-5

© 1993 United Feature Syndicate, Inc.

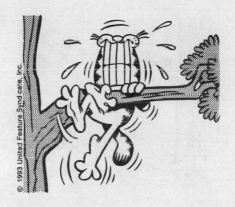

© 1993 United Feature Syndicate, Inc.

JIM DAVIS 2-10

© 1993 United Feature Syndicate, Inc.

© 1993 United Feature Syndicate, Inc.

© 1993 United Feature Syndicate, Inc.

© 1993 United Feature Syndicate, Inc.

PITIFUL

GRINKA

© 1993 United Feature Syndicate, Inc.

FEED ME

JIM DAVIS 3-19

© 1993 United Feature Syndicate, Inc.

© 1993 United Feature Syndicate, Inc.

© 1993 United Feature Syndicate, Inc.

© 1993 United Feature Syndicate, Inc.

JIM DAVIS 4-7

© 1993 United Feature Syndicate, Inc.

JIM DAViS 4-12

© 1993 United Feature Syndicate, Inc.

© 1993 United Feature Syndicate, Inc.

JIM DAVIS 4-29

© 1993 United Feature Syndicate, Inc.

© 1993 United Feature Syndicate, Inc.

© 1993 United Feature Syndicate, Inc.

© 1993 United Feature Syndicate, Inc.

© 1993 United Feature Syndicate, Inc.

SO, HOW'D THE DATE GO?

JIM DAVIS 5-21

OTHER GARFIELD BOOKS IN THIS SERIES

No. 1 Garfield The Great Lover   £2.99
No. 2 Garfield Why Do You Hate Mondays?   £2.99
No. 3 Garfield Does Pooky Need You?   £2.50
No. 4 Garfield Admit It, Odie's OK!   £2.99
No. 5 Garfield Two's Company   £2.50
No. 6 Garfield What's Cooking?   £2.50
No. 7 Garfield Who's Talking?   £2.99
No. 8 Garfield Strikes Again   £2.50
No. 9 Garfield Here's Looking At You   £2.50
No. 10 Garfield We Love You Too   £2.99
No. 11 Garfield Here We Go Again   £2.50
No. 12 Garfield Life And Lasagne   £2.99
No. 13 Garfield In The Pink   £2.50
No. 14 Garfield Just Good Friends   £2.50
No. 15 Garfield Plays It Again   £2.50
No. 16 Garfield Flying High   £2.50
No. 17 Garfield On Top Of The World   £2.50
No. 18 Garfield Happy Landings   £2.50
No. 19 Garfield Going Places   £2.99
No. 20 Garfield Le Magnifique!   £2.99
No. 21 Garfield In The Fast Lane   £2.99
No. 22 Garfield In Tune   £2.99
No. 23 Garfield The Reluctant Romeo   £2.99
No. 24 Garfield With Love From Me To You   £2.99
No. 25 Garfield A Gift For You   £2.99
No. 26 Garfield Great Impressions   £2.50
No. 27 Garfield Pick Of The Bunch   £2.99
No. 28 Garfield Light Of My Life   £2.99
No. 29 Garfield Hangs On   £2.99
No. 31 Garfield Says It With Flowers   £2.99
No. 32 Garfield Wave Rebel   £2.99
No. 33 Garfield Let's Party   £2.99
No. 34 Garfield On The Right Track   £2.99

Garfield Diet Book   £2.99
The Garfield Birthday Book   £2.99
Garfield's How To Party Book   £2.99
Garfield The Me Book   £2.99
Garfield's Big Fat Book Of Jokes & Riddles   £2.95

COLOUR TV SPECIALS

Garfield On The Town	£2.95
A Garfield Christmas	£3.99
Garfield's Thanksgiving	£2.95
Gallery 3	£2.99
Gallery 5	£2.99

GARFIELD THEME BOOKS

Garfield's Guide to Behaving Badly	£3.99
Garfield's Guide to Insults	£3.99
Garfield's Guide to Pigging Out	£3.99
Garfield's Guide to Romance	£3.99

All Ravette books are available at your local bookshop or from the address below. Just tick the titles required and send the form with your remittance to:-

B.B.C.S., P.O. BOX 941, HULL, NORTH HUMBERSIDE HU1 3YQ
24 Hour Telephone Credit Card Line 01482 224626
Prices and availability are subject to change without notice.

Please enclose a cheque or postal order made payable to B.B.C.S. to the value of the cover price of the book and allow the following for postage and packing:

U.K. & B.F.P.O: £1.00 for the first book and 50p for each additional book to a maximum of £3.50.

Overseas &   £2.00 for the first book, £1.00 for the second
Eire   and 50p for each additional book.

BLOCK CAPITALS PLEASE

Name ....

Address...

....

....

Cards accepted: Mastercard and Visa

```
┌──┬──┬──┬──┬──┬──┬──┬──┬──┬──┬──┬──┬──┬──┬──┬──┐
│  │  │  │  │  │  │  │  │  │  │  │  │  │  │  │  │
└──┴──┴──┴──┴──┴──┴──┴──┴──┴──┴──┴──┴──┴──┴──┴──┘
```

........Signature ....